PENGUIN BOOKS

BE A BLOODY TRAIN DRIVER

Jacky Fleming went to a suffragette school in London. She emerged awesomely uneducated because of the teachers' inexplicable preference for Latin as a first language. A year at Chelsea School of Art and a degree in fine art at Leeds University greatly improved her table-football technique. Other qualifications include A– for posture and a silver medal in Latin-American dancing. A brief stint in the art department of a London periodical was followed by eleven years teaching art as a foreign language. Jacky lives in Yorkshire and hates cooking.

Her cartoons have been published by the BBC, the Women's Press, Virago, Leeds Postcards, Aberdeen University Press, Longman, *Spare Rib* and others.

JACKY FLEMING

Be a bloody train driver

PENGUIN BOOKS

PENGUIN BOOKS

Published by the Penguin Group
Penguin Books Ltd, 27 Wrights Lane, London W8 5TZ, England
Penguin Books USA Inc., 375 Hudson Street, New York, New York 10014, USA
Penguin Books Australia Ltd, Ringwood, Victoria, Australia
Penguin Books Canada Ltd, 10 Alcorn Avenue, Toronto, Ontario, Canada M4V 3B2
Penguin Books (NZ) Ltd, 182–190 Wairau Road, Auckland 10, New Zealand

Penguin Books Ltd, Registered Offices: Harmondsworth, Middlesex, England

This collection first published in book form 1991
3 5 7 9 10 8 6 4 2

Copyright © Jacky Fleming, 1991
All rights reserved

The moral right of the author has been asserted

Printed in England by Clays Ltd, St Ives plc

Contents

Sugar and Spice   1

Because You're a Boy   10

Self-defence   29

Just When You Thought
It Couldn't Get Worse ...   39

Bundle of Joy   44

Jobs for the Girls   53

Consuming Passions   65

Happy Ever After   79

Sugar and Spice

when I grow up

you won't

and what are you going to be
when you grow up, little girl?
HORRIBLE
JF

worms

4

you said wear a dress

Come on, Malcolm, take it like a girl

my friend fancies you

does she?

christ it's gone cloudy

9

Because You're a Boy

What do women like BEST in a man?

11

14

JF

Colin needs a kick in the teeth

JF

15

where's my dinner?
it must be around somewhere, dear, where did you last see it?
JF

why do you want me to say I love you
when it's obvious?

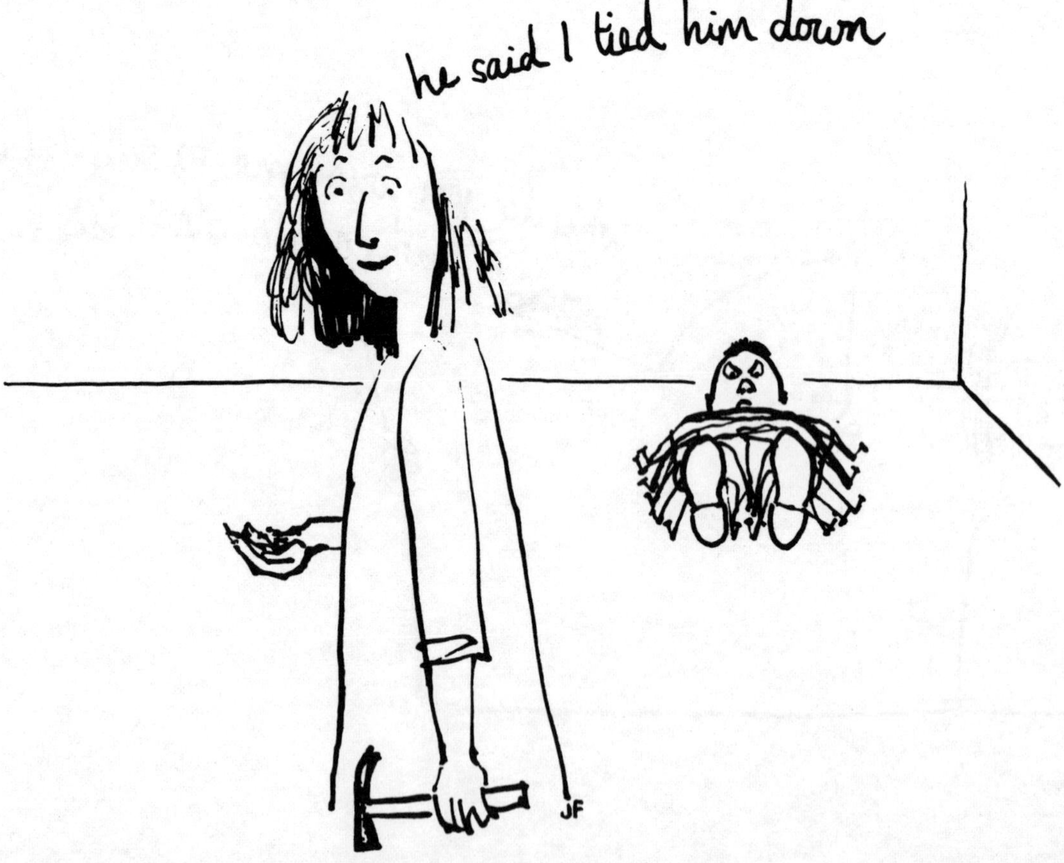
he said I tied him down
JF

it started when he moved in with me

19

......then he said why was I always trying to **CHANGE** him and I said probably because he's such an obnoxious thoughtless selfish overbearing self-righteous hypocritical arrogant loudmouthed misogynist bastard...

every woman needs a man to look after her

21

I expect it means Freud wished he had a bigger one, dear

24

The NEW Man

It's not pornography, it's a CELEBRATION of women through physical observations and contains articles of high calibre by the most prestigious contemporary writers and if I haven't succeeded in convincing you, I have at least convinced myself

27

where are those old-fashioned men
who'd be gone before breakfast?

Self-defence

I learnt some of it at
self-defence and the rest
I made up myself

JF

I've told you before—
you can't leave him
tied up in the garden

30

but he asked for it

31

KILL

JF

she bites

where I like
when I like
in whatever
I like
to wear

If men can't be trusted on the streets at night

then why aren't THEY kept in?

Georgie Porgie pudding and pie
Kissed the girls and made them cry

don't even THINK about it

as Judge Senile not only BLATANTLY FLAUNTED his stupidity and incompetence, but was also PROVOCATIVELY dressed in a WIG and GOWN, we can only assume he was inviting violent assault

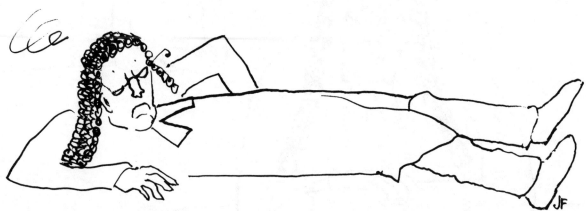

38

Just When You Thought It Couldn't Get Worse...

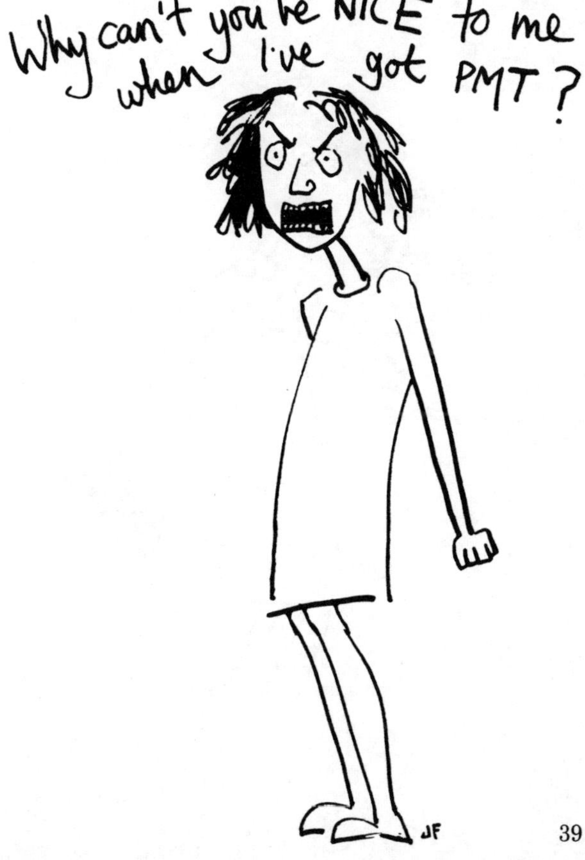

PMT SURVIVAL KIT

NOT FOR YOU FOR **ME**

PMT SURVIVAL KIT I

vital

HORSE TRANQUIL

may help a bit

EVENING PRIMROSE

will help a lot

WHISK

PMT SURVIVAL KIT II

Dear _____,
    I have had enough.
Everything is too dreadful.

It is not entirely your fault.

    Goodbye,

PMT SURVIVAL KIT III

CUT HERE

STICK ON CARD

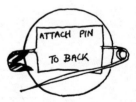

ATTACH PIN TO BACK

Of course the INTERESTING thing about PMT is that other people don't know you've got it because you LOOK perfectly NORMAL

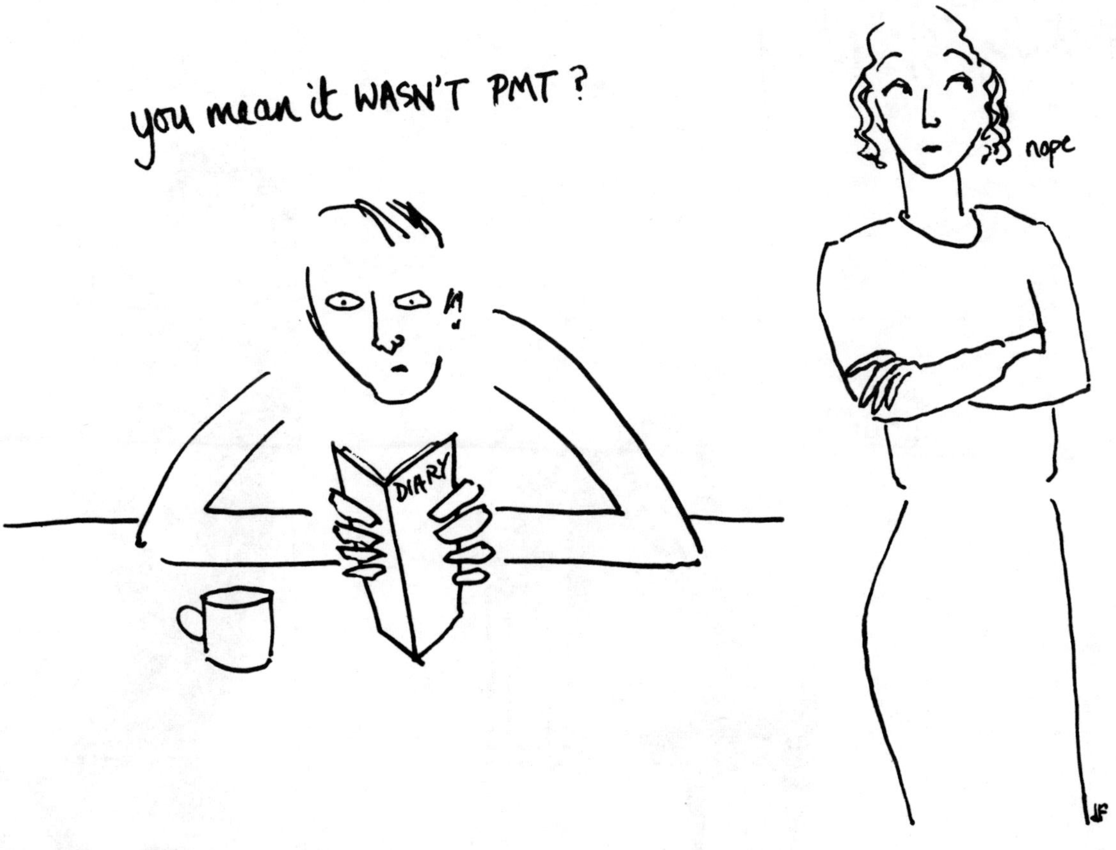
you mean it WASN'T PMT ?
nope
DIARY
JF

Bundle of Joy

is this your substitute for children?

no it's a domestic cat

JF

I've asked for a full anaesthetic

Doesn't she make you want one?

several

think of a beautiful flower opening

47

Our daughter doesn't attend school, we prefer the dating agency for underage smokers.

JF

49

and with us tonight we have Sandra
who GENUINELY has **NO** desire to have children

Why have there been no great women artists?
— 'Great questions by great men' series

i've changed my mind

Jobs for the Girls

you may call me old fashioned.....

I didn't, I called you an obstructive opinionated sexist bigot.

if you think you recognize
Daddy just give him a
goodnight kiss

and may the best man win,
Mrs Smith

JF

since I got the job Nigel's
been campaigning non-stop
for nursery provision

60

No, the briefcase does not contain tampax, Valium, and the children's packed lunches – the carrier bag does

One has to reflect very seriously on all the implications of women working for instance —
WHO'S going to look after ME?

JF

you want me to look after a
family, work full time,
and LOOK GOOD?

I wish these feminists would stop whingeing and do something

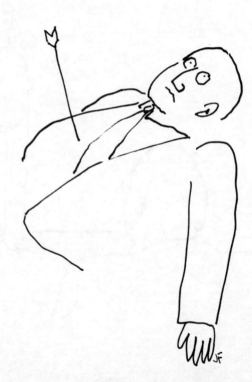

Consuming Passions

so I made it to 7 stone

BEFORE

...help

JF

AFTER

66

thirty one, thirty two...

68

It says if you do the ironing for 4 hours you can burn off the calories in 2 pieces of chocolate

tomorrow my life
will be transformed

if you can't beat 'em

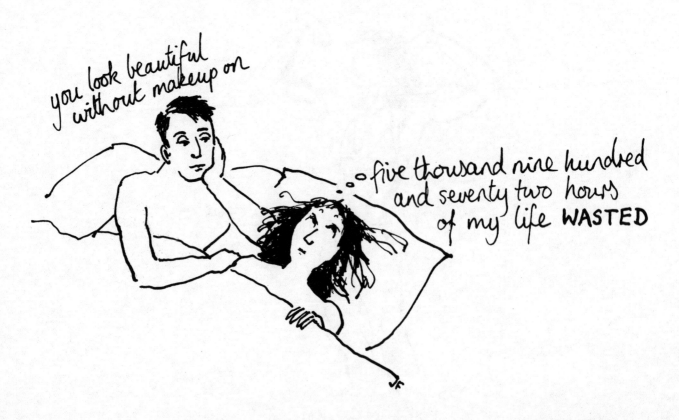

you look beautiful without makeup on

•••five thousand nine hundred and seventy two hours of my life WASTED

Happy Ever After

Once upon a time there was a beautiful princess....girls, please

You only have to
PRETEND he's a prince

Little Ms Muffet
Sat on a tuffet
Eating her curds and whey.
Along came a spider
And sat down beside her
So she squashed it.

Will the Prince remain a quivering blob of frogspawn
or will the kind Princess swallow some and
thereby save him? Probably not

the princess
and the pea

Haven't you got a dragon to slay or something else incredibly dangerous?

some day my prince will come

some day my prince will come

bog off

87

and they lived
happily ever after.....

never give up

JF

90